Excellence

in Fractions, Decimals and Percentages

Includes ratio and proportion

Year **6**

By Richard Cooper

RISING STARS

Rising Stars UK Ltd., 76 Farnaby Road, Bromley,
BR1 4BH

Website: **www.risingstars-uk.com**

All facts are correct at time of going to press.

Published 2004
Text, design and layout ©Rising Stars UK Ltd.

Editorial: Tanya Solomons
Design: Ken Vail Graphic Design
Character illustration: © Louisa Burville-Riley
Technical illustration: © Marc Burville-Riley
Cover photo: © Richard Drury/Getty Images

British Library Cataloguing in Publication Data
A CIP record for this book is available from the
British Library.

ISBN 1-904591-51-5

Printed by Wyndeham Gait, Grimsby, UK.

Contents

How to use this book

The *Excellence in Fractions, Decimals and Percentages with Ratio and Proportion* series is designed to help you get to grips with this tricky topic.

The key thing to remember about fractions, decimals and percentages is:

> **They are all different ways of expressing the same amount.**

For example:

25% is the same as $\frac{1}{4}$ which is also the same as **0.25**.

The introduction

This section of each page gives you an idea of the sort of problems you are likely to see and helps you to understand what maths you need to use.

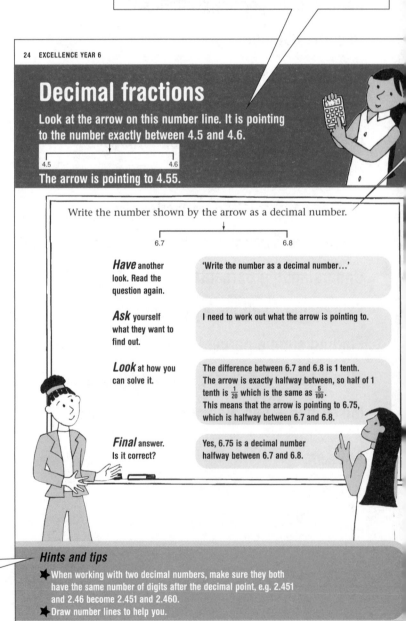

Decimal fractions

Look at the arrow on this number line. It is pointing to the number exactly between 4.5 and 4.6.

4.5 ——————— 4.6

The arrow is pointing to 4.55.

Write the number shown by the arrow as a decimal number.

6.7 ——————— 6.8

Have another look. Read the question again.

'Write the number as a decimal number...'

Ask yourself what they want to find out.

I need to work out what the arrow is pointing to.

Look at how you can solve it.

The difference between 6.7 and 6.8 is 1 tenth. The arrow is exactly halfway between, so half of 1 tenth is $\frac{1}{20}$ which is the same as $\frac{5}{100}$. This means that the arrow is pointing to 6.75, which is halfway between 6.7 and 6.8.

Final answer. Is it correct?

Yes, 6.75 is a decimal number halfway between 6.7 and 6.8.

Hints and tips

★ When working with two decimal numbers, make sure they both have the same number of digits after the decimal point, e.g. 2.451 and 2.46 become 2.451 and 2.460.
★ Draw number lines to help you.

Hints and tips

The hints and tips section gives you useful ideas for completing the problems on the other page. These are the things you need to remember if you are doing a quiz or test!

The example problem

The flow chart takes you through an example step–by–step. This is important when you are answering questions about fractions, decimals, percentages (and ratio and proportion).

Every time you approach a fractions question, remember these four steps:

Have another look. Read the question again.

Ask yourself what they want you to find out.

Look at how you can solve it.

Final answer. Is it correct?

We can remember this by looking at the first letter of each step.

They read HALF!

Look at these number lines. What decimal fraction are the arrows pointing to?

a)
3.7   3.8   ☐

b)
11.1   11.2   ☐

c)
4.2   4.3   ☐

d)
21.2   21.3   ☐

e)
10.7   10.8   ☐

f)
54.4   54.5   ☐

g)
18.9   19   ☐

h)
29.1   29.2   ☐

i)
25.5   25.6   ☐

j)
7.6   7.7   ☐

Suggest a decimal fraction between the following numbers.

a) 7.35 and 7.36

b) 673.84 and 673.85

c) 55.55 and 55.56

d) 892.72 and 892.73

e) 11.13 and 11.14

Challenge

a) Write two decimal fractions that these numbers are exactly halfway between.

8.5

23.35

125.05

b) Suggest a decimal fraction to go between these numbers.

4.675   4.68   4.7   4.9   5

The questions

The questions get harder as you go down the page.

- Section 1 questions are fairly straightforward and help you to practise your skills.
- Section 2 questions are a bit harder but will help you to remember all the key points.
- The Challenge sections are really tough and sometimes mean that you can make up games and your own questions! They can be great fun!

Ten top tips

1   Work through each question step–by–step. Follow the flow chart.

Have another look.
Read the question again.

Ask yourself what they
want you to find out.

Look at how you can solve it.

Final answer. Is it correct?

2   Always *show your working* or 'method'. This will help you to keep track of what you have done and may help you to get extra marks.

3   Always *include your units* in the answer. If you don't, you won't get full marks.

4   When you first read through a question, *underline important words and numbers*. This will help you to remember the important bits!

5 *Draw a picture* to help you. Sometimes a
   question is easier if you can 'see' it.
   Drawing 6 apples can help you if you need
   to divide them!

6 If the problem has a number of steps,
   break it down and do *one step at a time.*

7 When *checking your answers,*
   look at the inverse operation.

8 Sometimes an answer will 'sound right'. Read it
   out (quietly) and listen. *Does it make sense?*

9 If you are using measurements (grams,
   litres, cm), make sure that the *units are
   the same* before you calculate.

10 Once again! *Read the
   question again.*

Changing improper fractions to mixed numbers

An improper fraction is a fraction where the denominator is bigger than the numerator.

You need to be able to change these to a 'mixed number'.

Mixed numbers are whole numbers and fractions together.

$\frac{33}{8}$ as a mixed number is 4 and $\frac{1}{8}$.

8 fits into 33 four times with one eighth left over. We write this as $4\frac{1}{8}$.

Change the improper fraction $\frac{37}{10}$ to a mixed number.

Have another look. Read the question again.

> '*Improper* fraction and *mixed* number…'

Ask yourself what they want you to find out.

> Change 37 tenths into a mixed number…

Look at how you can solve it.

> 37 divided by 10 is 3 with 7 remaining.

Final answer. Is it correct?

> $3\frac{7}{10}$ Yes, that is the correct mixed number.

Hints and tips

★ Look at the fraction part of a mixed number. Has it got a simpler equivalent?

$6\frac{5}{10}$ is the same as $6\frac{1}{2}$

★ Practise turning mixed numbers into improper fractions.

$3\frac{1}{4}$ is $\frac{13}{4}$. All you do is multiply the denominator by the whole number and add the numerator.

Turn these improper fractions into mixed numbers.

a) $\frac{15}{4}$

b) $\frac{62}{6}$

c) $\frac{31}{3}$

d) $\frac{56}{13}$

e) $\frac{46}{5}$

f) $\frac{34}{11}$

g) $\frac{63}{8}$

h) $\frac{77}{9}$

i) $\frac{41}{13}$

j) $\frac{100}{18}$

Now turn these mixed numbers into improper fractions.

a) $7\frac{3}{8}$

b) $72\frac{9}{13}$

c) $27\frac{3}{7}$

d) $91\frac{1}{9}$

e) $53\frac{5}{6}$

Challenge

Seven and a quarter pizzas were eaten at Laura's party. How many twelfths of pizza were eaten in total?

Fourteen and a third cream cakes were eaten for dessert! How many sixths of cream cake is this in total?

Dad said he would give me $\frac{9}{5}$ of £5 or £6.50 if I washed the car. Which one is the greater? By how much?

Relationships between fractions

Look at these fraction bars.

They show that $\frac{1}{2}$ is twice as much as one quarter.
Now look at this bar.

$\frac{1}{2}$ is three times as much as $\frac{1}{6}$.

Complete this sentence: $\frac{1}{4}$ is twice as much as …

Have another look. Read the question again.

'Twice as much…'

Ask yourself what they want you to find out.

I need to find what is half of $\frac{1}{4}$.

Look at how you can solve it.

I need to draw a picture here.

First colour in $\frac{1}{4}$ of one.
Now I must colour in $\frac{1}{2}$ of $\frac{1}{4}$.

That must be $\frac{1}{8}$.

Final answer. Is it correct?

Check the drawing. Is it correct? Yes! I've got it right.

Hints and tips

★ Think about the links.
$\frac{1}{2}$ is twice as much as $\frac{1}{4}$. $\frac{1}{4}$ is twice as much as $\frac{1}{8}$.
The larger the denominator, the smaller the fraction.

Look at these fractions.
Write 'twice as much as' or 'half as much as' in the spaces.

a) $\frac{1}{4}$ _____ $\frac{1}{2}$

b) $\frac{1}{4}$ _____ $\frac{1}{8}$

c) $\frac{1}{5}$ _____ $\frac{1}{10}$

d) $\frac{1}{3}$ _____ $\frac{1}{6}$

e) $\frac{1}{20}$ _____ $\frac{1}{10}$

Draw fraction bars to solve these.

f) $\frac{1}{8}$ is half as much as

g) $\frac{1}{10}$ is twice as much as

h) $\frac{1}{2}$ is ten times as much as

i) $\frac{1}{3}$ is three times as much as

j) $\frac{1}{4}$ is three times a much as

Complete these number sentences.

a) $\frac{2}{5}$ is twice as much as

b) $\frac{3}{4}$ is twice as much as

c) $\frac{1}{10}$ is ten times as much as

d) $\frac{1}{100}$ is half as much as

e) $\frac{1}{20}$ is half as much as

Challenge

a) I have 12 drinks on a tray. $\frac{1}{6}$ of the drinks are lemonade. There are
twice as many cola as lemonade. What fraction of the drinks are cola?

b) I have 16 doughnuts in a bag. $\frac{1}{2}$ are jam and there are four times
as many jam as vanilla. What fraction of the doughnuts are vanilla?

Reducing fractions – cancelling

Look at this fraction equivalent statement: $\frac{2}{3} = \frac{8}{12}$

We can reduce a fraction down to its simplest form by finding a number which divides exactly into the top and bottom number.

$\frac{8}{12}$ can be made simpler by dividing the numerator and the denominator by 4.

$8 \div 4 = 2$ $\qquad$ $12 \div 4 = 3$ $\qquad$ So, $\frac{8}{12} = \frac{2}{3}$

Reduce this fraction to its lowest possible form: $\frac{12}{16}$

Have another look. Read the question again.

'Reduce... $\frac{12}{16}$ ...'

Ask yourself what they want you to find out.

I need to reduce the fraction $\frac{12}{16}$ to its lowest form.

Look at how you can solve it.

What is the highest number that divides into 12 and 16? OK, 4. 12 divided by 4 is 3 and 16 divided by 4 is 4. The answer is $\frac{3}{4}$.

Final answer. Is it correct?

Yes, I've read the question again and my answer is correct.

Hints and tips

★ When you are looking for numbers that divide into the top and bottom numbers, start with 2. Are the numerator and denominator both even numbers?

★ Remember the prime numbers (a number that can only be divided by itself and 1) The only prime number that can be reduced is 2.

1 Reduce these fractions to their lowest form.

a) $\frac{9}{12}$

b) $\frac{15}{25}$

c) $\frac{10}{20}$

d) $\frac{12}{48}$

e) $\frac{8}{10}$

f) $\frac{14}{20}$

g) $\frac{6}{18}$

h) $\frac{16}{48}$

i) $\frac{7}{21}$

j) $\frac{18}{24}$

2 Reduce these fractions to their simplest form.

a) $\frac{45}{54}$

b) $\frac{75}{195}$

c) $\frac{12}{96}$

d) $\frac{96}{336}$

e) $\frac{69}{108}$

★ Challenge

Write down 5 equivalent fractions for each of the following.
However, none of your equivalents are allowed to
be double the previous one.

$\frac{1}{3}$

$\frac{1}{5}$

$\frac{8}{7}$

$\frac{5}{8}$

Common denominators

Look at these three fractions and decide which one is the biggest.

$$\frac{1}{2} \qquad \frac{5}{6} \qquad \frac{9}{12}$$

To do this you need to convert all the fractions so they have the same denominator.

Which of these fractions is the biggest? $\frac{2}{3}, \frac{3}{4}, \frac{5}{6}.$

Have another look. Read the question again.

'Which is the biggest?'

Ask yourself what they want you to find out.

I need to convert all the fractions so they have the same denominator and order them.

Look at how you can solve it.

The lowest number that all three denominators (3, 4 and 6) will divide into is 12.

Now I multiply the numerators by the same number I multiplied the denominator by to reach 12.

So, $\frac{2}{3} = \frac{8}{12}$ $\qquad \frac{3}{4} = \frac{9}{12}$ $\qquad \frac{5}{6} = \frac{10}{12}$

Now I can mark these on a number line.

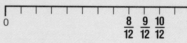

The largest fraction is $\frac{5}{6}$.

Final answer. Is it correct?

Yes, I've read the question again and my answer is correct.

Hints and tips

★ Look at the denominators first. See how, or if, they relate to each other. What is the *lowest* number they will all divide into?

Convert these pairs of fractions so they have a common denominator. Circle the largest one.

a) $\frac{2}{3}$ $\frac{3}{4}$

b) $\frac{4}{5}$ $\frac{8}{9}$

c) $\frac{5}{6}$ $\frac{6}{7}$

d) $\frac{2}{5}$ $\frac{3}{7}$

e) $\frac{7}{12}$ $\frac{4}{5}$

Convert these pairs of fractions so they have a common denominator.
Put = between them if they are equal.
Put > if the first fraction is greater than the second one.
Put < if the first fraction is smaller than the second one.

f) $\frac{4}{7}$ ☐ $\frac{4}{9}$ g) $\frac{1}{5}$ ☐ $\frac{2}{9}$ h) $\frac{1}{3}$ ☐ $\frac{3}{7}$ i) $\frac{2}{9}$ ☐ $\frac{3}{8}$ j) $\frac{3}{10}$ ☐ $\frac{4}{13}$

Put these sets of fractions in order from highest to lowest.

a) $\frac{1}{3}$ $\frac{3}{7}$ $\frac{2}{5}$

b) $\frac{3}{5}$ $\frac{5}{7}$ $\frac{2}{3}$

c) $\frac{7}{9}$ $\frac{3}{4}$ $\frac{5}{8}$

d) $\frac{7}{10}$ $\frac{4}{5}$ $\frac{7}{8}$

e) $\frac{1}{3}$ $\frac{3}{8}$ $\frac{7}{10}$

 Challenge

Place these numbers in order, starting with the smallest one.

$2\frac{1}{10}$ $1\frac{3}{10}$ $2\frac{2}{5}$ $1\frac{5}{6}$ $2\frac{1}{3}$

Finding fractions of numbers

Finding a fraction of a number is all about division and multiplication.

Finding $\frac{3}{4}$ of 12 means we have to find out what $\frac{1}{4}$ of 12 is first then multiply the answer by 3.

What is seven tenths of 200?

Have another look. Read the question again.	'Seven tenths of 200…'
Ask yourself what they want you to find out.	I need to find one tenth first and then multiply that by seven.
Look at how you can solve it.	One tenth of 200 is 20 (200 divided by 10). Now I multiply that answer by the numerator, which is seven. So, 7 x 20 = 140 Seven tenths of 200 = 140
Final answer. Is it correct?	Yes, I have checked my answer twice and it *looks* correct.

Hints and tips

★ If you are asked to find a fraction of a quantity such as metres, convert the quantity into its smallest units first, e.g. 2 metres becomes 200 cm. You can then convert your final answer back to the original unit.

★ What fraction of 1 kg is 400 g? With this sort of question, the 400 g is the numerator and the 1 kg is the denominator. So it becomes $\frac{400}{1000}$.

1

Find the fractions of these numbers.

a) $\frac{2}{5}$ of 25

b) $\frac{5}{6}$ of 42

c) $\frac{4}{7}$ of 35

d) $\frac{5}{8}$ of 32

e) $\frac{7}{9}$ of 63

f) $\frac{3}{10}$ of 90

g) $\frac{7}{10}$ of 50

h) $\frac{11}{100}$ of 500

i) $\frac{17}{100}$ of 600

j) $\frac{37}{100}$ of 800

2

Find the fractions of these quantities.

a) $\frac{5}{7}$ of 140 kilometres

b) $\frac{4}{9}$ of 54 kilograms

c) $\frac{7}{8}$ of 960 metres

d) $\frac{3}{5}$ of 1020 centimetres

e) $\frac{57}{100}$ of 1500 litres

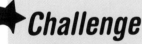 **Challenge**

a) Jack has run $\frac{7}{10}$ of his total distance for the 1500 m.

How far does he still have to go?

b) Kate still needs to run $\frac{3}{4}$ of the 1500 m race.

How far has she travelled so far?

c) Maria has nearly finished her race. She has travelled $\frac{9}{10}$ of the 1500 m.

How much further ahead of Jack is she?

Ratio and proportion problems

Look at this tile pattern.

The *ratio* of white tiles to black is 1 to every 2.
We write this as 1 : 2
The *proportion* of white tiles in the whole line is
1 in 3. We can write this as a fraction: $\frac{1}{3}$

Ratio and proportion problems can be asked in a 'story' form like this.

Jessie shares out 12 marbles. She gives Leo 1 marble for every 3 marbles that she takes. How many marbles does Leo get?

Have another look. Read the question again.

'12 marbles... 1 for every 3...'

Ask yourself what they want you to find out.

I need to find out how many marbles Jessie gives to Leo.

Look at how you can solve it.

OK, think clearly and picture the numbers...
Jessie is sharing 4 marbles at a time. Every time she gets 3, Leo gets 1. There are 12 marbles so Jessie can do this 3 times (12 ÷ 4 = 3).
Leo receives 3 marbles from Jessie.

Final answer. Is it correct?

I have checked my answer twice and it looks correct. I can also check by counting out the problem in real life – I don't have to use marbles, any objects will do.

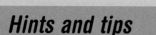

Hints and tips

★ Ratios can be written using a colon (:) to separate the numbers. The : means 'to every'.
★ Proportions are usually written as a fraction. For example, $\frac{1}{3}$ means 'one in every three'.

What is the ratio of black tiles to white tiles?
What is the proportion of black tiles in each pattern?

	Ratio	Proportion			Ratio	Proportion
a)			b)			
c)			d)			
e)			f)			
g)			h)			
i)			j)			

What is the ratio of black squares to white squares in these patterns?
What is the proportion of black squares in each pattern?

	Ratio	Proportion
a)		
b)		
c)		
d)		
e)		

Challenge

a) Hannah has 15 sweets. She gives 2 sweets to Sally for every one she takes.
   How many sweets does Sally get?

b) In Chestnut Class there are 25 children. There are 2 girls for every 3 boys.
   How many boys are there in the class? How many girls are there?

c) In the ball pond there are 5 green balls for every 3 red balls.
   If there are 48 balls altogether, how many green balls are there?

Decimal notation

Look at this number – 42.793. Each digit represents a number depending which column it is in.

42.793

The first column to the right of the decimal point is the tenths column.

The second column to the right of the decimal point is the hundredths column.

The third column to the right of the decimal point is the thousandths column.

Perform this calculation. Line up the digits in the correct columns.

372.7 + 61.89

Have another look. Read the question again.

372.7 + 61.89… It's addition.

Ask yourself what they want you to find out.

I need to add them together and make sure I line up the digits and decimal points correctly.

Look at how you can solve it.

Estimate an answer first: 370 + 60 = 430
(It will be easier if I add a zero to the .7 so I have the same amount of digits in each column)

```
   372.70
+   61.89
  ───────
  434.59
```

Final answer. Is it correct?

Yes, my answer is close to my estimate. I have lined the digits up in the correct columns. (My answer would have been significantly different if I had not.)

Hints and tips

★ Start by lining up the decimal points and then write in the digits for the calculation.

★ Adding a zero (or zeros) to level the number of digits in each column is a very useful way to avoid simple errors when calculating.

1

Complete these calculations.

a) 3.7 + 4.9

b) 33.9 + 3.9

c) 12.8 + 3.5

d) 52.77 − 29.29

e) 47.6 − 13.4

f) 84.5 − 9.97

g) 72.8 − 19.9

h) 28.73 + 79.4

i) 64.7 + 6.6

j) 61.12 + 99.1

2

Complete these calculations of quantities.

a) 4.736 litres + 6.23 litres

b) 62.719 kg − 3.67 kg

c) 8.698 km + 2.77 km

d) 81.2 km − 8.773 km

e) 52.526 kg + 8.9 kg

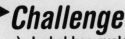 *Challenge*

a) Isobel has cycled 18.367 km and Toby has cycled 13.93 km.
    How much further has Isobel travelled than Toby?

b) Steve has three pumpkins. The first weighs 0.45 kg, the second 0.58 kg and the
    final one a huge 1.23 kg. How much do his three pumpkins weigh altogether?

c) Tanya has 7.453 l of red paint. She also has 3.04 l of blue paint and
    9.289 l of white paint. How much paint does she have altogether?

Decimal digits

Look at this number: **35.829**

nine thousandths

Three tens

five units

eight tenths

2 hundredths

Each digit has a value because of its position.

What is the value of the circled digit in this number?

72.1⬡93

Have another look. Read the question again.

'Value… circled digit… 72.193…'

Ask yourself what they want you to find out.

I need to find the value of the circled digit, 9.

Look at how you can solve it.

The numbers to the left of the decimal point are always whole numbers. The first column to the right is tenths, the next is hundredths and the next is thousandths. The digit 9 is in the hundredths column. The value of the digit is 9 hundredths or $\frac{9}{100}$.

Final answer. Is it correct?

Yes, I have checked my answer and it looks correct.

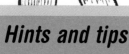

Hints and tips

★ Remember, digits to the *left* of the decimal point represent *whole* numbers.

★ Digits to the *right* of the decimal point represent *fractions of a whole*.

Try to picture the columns in your mind.

What do the circled digits represent?

a) 0.⑥2   b) 4.8①   c) ⑧.90   d) 5.⑤5   e) 7.③9

f) 21.1②1   g) 7.83⑤   h) 8④2   i) 7.⑨81   j) 0.00①

Write the decimal fractions equivalent to the following.

a) Four tenths, two hundredths and eight thousandths

b) Nine tenths, nine hundredths and two thousandths

c) Eighteen and twenty-five thousandths

d) Six and six thousandths

e) One and one hundred and eleven thousandths

 Challenge

Convert these to decimal fractions and calculate the sums.

a) Eight tenths, one hundredth and nine thousandths + one tenth, eight hundredths and one thousandth

b) Three and eighteen hundredths + two and three tenths

c) Add just the circled digits.

2.6⑦9 + 3.10⑤ + 5.9③6 + ①235

Decimal fractions

Look at the arrow on this number line. It is pointing to the number exactly between 4.5 and 4.6.

4.5   4.6

The arrow is pointing to 4.55.

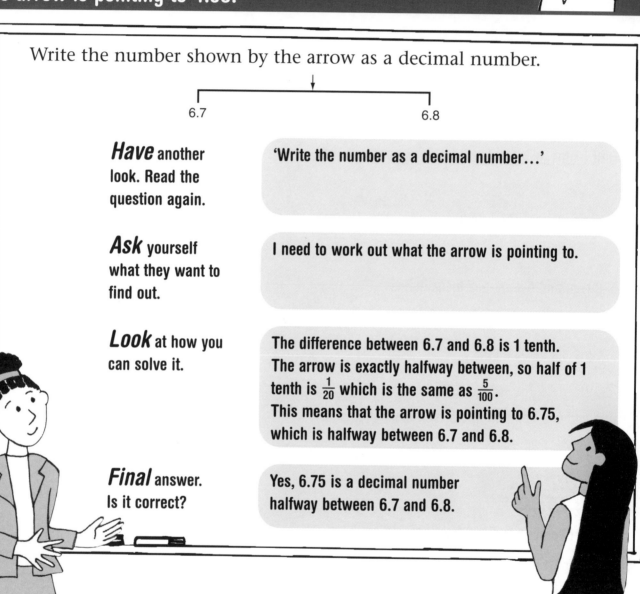

Write the number shown by the arrow as a decimal number.

6.7   6.8

Have another look. Read the question again.

'Write the number as a decimal number…'

Ask yourself what they want to find out.

I need to work out what the arrow is pointing to.

Look at how you can solve it.

The difference between 6.7 and 6.8 is 1 tenth. The arrow is exactly halfway between, so half of 1 tenth is $\frac{1}{20}$ which is the same as $\frac{5}{100}$. This means that the arrow is pointing to 6.75, which is halfway between 6.7 and 6.8.

Final answer. Is it correct?

Yes, 6.75 is a decimal number halfway between 6.7 and 6.8.

Hints and tips

★ When working with two decimal numbers, make sure they both have the same number of digits after the decimal point, e.g. 2.451 and 2.46 become 2.451 and 2.460.

★ Draw number lines to help you.

1

Look at these number lines. What decimal fraction are the arrows pointing to?

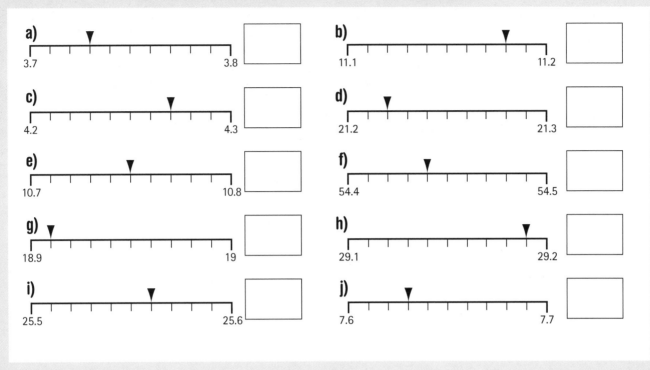

a) 3.7 — 3.8

b) 11.1 — 11.2

c) 4.2 — 4.3

d) 21.2 — 21.3

e) 10.7 — 10.8

f) 54.4 — 54.5

g) 18.9 — 19

h) 29.1 — 29.2

i) 25.5 — 25.6

j) 7.6 — 7.7

2

Suggest a decimal fraction between the following numbers.

a) 7.35 and 7.36

b) 673.84 and 673.85

c) 55.55 and 55.56

d) 892.72 and 892.73

e) 11.13 and 11.14

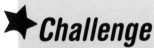

Challenge

a) Write two decimal fractions that these numbers are exactly halfway between.

8.5

23.35

125.05

b) Suggest a decimal fraction to go between these numbers.

4.675 _____ 4.68 _____ 4.7 _____ 4.9 _____ 5

Ordering numbers to 3 decimal places

When ordering decimals, work methodically. First look at the whole numbers, then the tenths, then the hundredths and so on.

Can you put the measurements of these javelin throws in order, longest first?

Greg	Martina	Tim	Boris	Serena
5.25m	15.3m	5.78m	5.874m	5.2m

Have another look. Read the question again.

'Longest first…'

Ask yourself what they want you to find out.

I need to order the measurements by size – longest to shortest.

Look at how you can solve it.

15 is the highest whole number – that's Martina.
Next there are four measurements of 5 metres, so I move to the tenths column…
The largest tenth is Boris so he is second, then Tim so he is third.
Greg and Serena both have 2 tenths so I move to the hundredths column…
Greg has 5 hundredths and Serena doesn't have any so Greg is fourth and Serena is fifth.

Final answer. Is it correct?

I can write the measurements in order to check if I am correct.

Hints and tips

★ Work methodically – carefully and step-by-step.
★ Always work from left to right when ordering numbers.
  You can add zeros to a number if it helps, e.g. '5.2' is the same as '5.20'.

Order these sets of decimals – largest first.

a) 4.4, 4.44, 4.7, 44.04

b) 98.8, 89.9, 99.9, 98.9

c) 54.5, 45.5, 55.54, 45.55

d) 24.42, 24,24, 42.4, 42.42

e) 72.27, 7.27, 77.22, 17.22

f) 0.01, 1.01, 0.1, 10.01

g) 61.1, 61.12, 12.6, 12.66

h) 9.9, 0.09, 0.99, 99.09

Order these decimals, smallest first.

a) 7.765, 7.675, 6.765, 6.776, 7.756, 6.667, 7.676

b) 9.919, 9.119, 9.999, 9.191, 1.991, 9.991, 9.909

c) 5.055, 5.505, 5.555, 5.005, 5.050, 5.550, 5.155

d) 84.448, 84.844, 84.484, 48.884, 84.888, 8.448

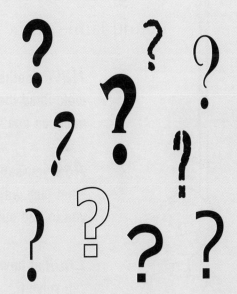

Challenge

Order these decimals, largest first. Then work out the difference between the smallest and the largest decimal.

a) 6.445, 64.545, 65.465, 6.045, 6.505, 66.556

b) 101.011, 110.101, 101.11, 111.001, 101.101, 11.011

c) 75.67, 67.57, 55.77, 77.55, 77.67, 76.66

Rounding numbers

Finley's time for the 400m is 63.78 seconds.
If we round Finley's time to the nearest whole
number then it is 64 seconds.

> Because the .78 means we round up
> to the next whole number, which is 64.

If we round Finley's time to the nearest tenth
then his time is 63.80 seconds.

> Because we round the .78 up to
> 80, which is the nearest tenth.

Jamie's time for the 400m is 66.26 seconds.

Round Jamie's time to the nearest tenth and to the nearest whole.

Have another look. Read the question again.	'Round to the nearest tenth and whole...'
Ask yourself what they want you to find out.	I need to round 66.26 to the nearest tenth and the nearest whole.
Look at how you can solve it.	The nearest tenth to .26 is 30. The nearest whole number to 66.26 is 66. I have to round the .26 down. (If it was .50 or above, I would round it up.)
Final answer. Is it correct?	Jamie's time to the nearest tenth is 66.30 seconds. His time to the nearest whole is 66 seconds.

Hints and tips

★ Remember that 5 always rounds UP.
★ The whole numbers are always to the LEFT of the decimal point.

1 Round these distances to the nearest tenth and the nearest whole.

a) 3.62 m

b) 10.34 km

c) 6.91 m

d) 52.52 km

e) 4.15 cm

f) 24.45 km

g) 9.78 cm

h) 89.68 km

i) 2.44 cm

j) 23.41 km

2 Round these numbers to the nearest tenth and the nearest whole.

a) 99.78

b) 110.71

c) 899.65

d) 999.89

e) 101.01

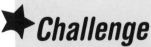

Challenge

Carol's times for the 100 m
12.89, 12.98, 12.08, 12.79,

Ann's times for the 100 m
12.56, 12.37, 12.65, 12.67

a) In the County trials the times are rounded to the nearest whole second.
Round these times to the nearest whole second. Was there a winner?

b) In the National trials the times are rounded to the nearest tenth of a second.
Who was the fastest in the Nationals?

Decimal and fraction equivalence

Fractions and decimals are related – they are just different ways of writing the same thing.

Look at these decimal and fraction equivalents:

0.5 is the same as $\frac{1}{2}$ 0.1 is the same as $\frac{1}{10}$

0.25 is the same as $\frac{1}{4}$ 0.01 is the same as $\frac{1}{100}$

0.125 is the same as $\frac{1}{8}$ 0.001 is the same as $\frac{1}{1000}$

0.75 is the same as $\frac{3}{4}$

Write $\frac{3}{8}$ as a decimal fraction.

Have another look. Read the question again.

'$\frac{3}{8}$... decimal fraction...'

Ask yourself what they want you to find out.

I need to convert $\frac{3}{8}$ into a decimal.

Look at how you can solve it.

I know that $\frac{1}{8}$ is the same as 0.125 so $\frac{3}{8}$ is 3 times 0.125.
0.125 x 3 = 0.375

Final answer. Is it correct?

Yes, 0.375 is correct. It is a little less than a half, as is $\frac{3}{8}$.

Hints and tips

★ It really helps if you learn as many fraction and decimal equivalents as you can. There are no short cuts – just do it! Start with the list above.

★ Other useful ones to learn are:
$\frac{1}{3} = 0.333$ so $\frac{2}{3} = 0.666$ and $\frac{1}{5} = 0.2$ so $\frac{2}{5} = 0.4$

Write these fractions as decimal fractions.

a) $\frac{2}{4}$

b) $\frac{9}{10}$

c) $\frac{3}{10}$

d) $\frac{7}{10}$

e) $\frac{7}{8}$

f) $\frac{3}{8}$

g) $\frac{2}{5}$

h) $\frac{31}{100}$

i) $\frac{4}{5}$

j) $\frac{7}{100}$

Write these as decimal fractions.

a) $\frac{7}{1000}$

b) $\frac{283}{1000}$

c) $\frac{27}{1000}$

d) $\frac{729}{1000}$

e) $\frac{107}{1000}$

 Challenge

Look at this statement:

$$\frac{800}{1000} = \frac{80}{100} = \frac{8}{10} = 0.8$$

Fill in the blanks.

a) $\frac{300}{1000} = \frac{\boxed{}}{\boxed{}} = \frac{\boxed{}}{\boxed{}} = \boxed{}.3$

b) $\frac{350}{1000} = \frac{\boxed{}}{100} = \frac{\boxed{}}{\boxed{}} = \boxed{}.\boxed{}$

Converting fractions to decimals using division

Fractions can be converted into decimals by dividing the top number (the numerator) by the bottom number (the denominator).
You will need a calculator to help you with these questions.

What is three quarters as a decimal fraction?

Have another look. Read the question again.

'Three quarters… decimal fraction…'

Ask yourself what they want you to find out.

I need to find out the decimal equivalent of $\frac{3}{4}$.

Look at how you can solve it.

With my calculator I enter: 3 ÷ 4 = My answer is 0.75.

Final answer. Is it correct?

I know my answer is correct because I remembered $\frac{3}{4} = 0.75$ when I learnt my fraction and decimal equivalents!

Hints and tips

★ When you use a calculator, always question what the display tells you. Does it look correct? If not, take a couple of seconds to redo the calculation and press the keys carefully.

★ Remember, decimals with whole numbers are the same as mixed fractions, e.g. 2.1 is the same as $2\frac{1}{10}$.

1

Convert these fractions to decimals. See if you can do it without
a calculator. (Use one if you have to!)

a) $\frac{1}{2}$

b) $\frac{3}{4}$

c) $\frac{1}{4}$

d) $\frac{2}{5}$

e) $\frac{1}{5}$

f) $\frac{2}{3}$

g) $\frac{1}{10}$

h) $\frac{3}{10}$

i) $\frac{1}{3}$

j) $\frac{7}{10}$

2

Try these word problems. Give your answer as a decimal fraction.

a) In a test, 60 out of 80 cats preferred 'Moggymeat' cat food.
What decimal fraction didn't prefer it?

b) McBlobby's burgers are half prime beef and the other half
prime grease. What decimal fraction of McBlobby's burgers
is prime grease?

c) In Australia, 75 people out of every 100 visit the beach at least
once a week. What decimal fraction of people doesn't visit the
beach each week?

d) Nine hundred out of a thousand people at a rugby match
bought a programme before the game. What decimal fraction
of people didn't buy a programme?

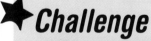 *Challenge*

Without a calculator, work out the following fractions as decimals.

a) $\frac{125}{500}$

b) $\frac{1700}{4250}$

c) $\frac{2825}{4520}$

Understanding percentages

The word 'percent' means 'parts per hundred'.
We use the % symbol for percent.

Draw a grid of a hundred squares. Now shade seventy-three squares. The ratio of the *number of shaded squares* to the *total number of squares* can be shown as a fraction.

Ratio ⟶ 73:100   Fraction ⟶ $\frac{73}{100}$

We can show this fraction as a percentage by adding % ⟶ 73%

Write 10% as a fraction, ratio and decimal.

Have another look. Read the question again.	'10%... fraction… ratio… decimal.'
Ask yourself what they want uou to find out.	I need to write 10% as a fraction, ratio and decimal.
Look at how you can solve it.	10% as a fraction = $\frac{10}{100}$ which is $\frac{1}{10}$ 10% as a ratio is 10 to 100 or 1:10 10% as a decimal is 0.10 or .1
Final answer. Is it correct?	Yes, I have given the three answers that are required.

Hints and tips

★ Percentages can be used to show the results of surveys or marks scored in a test. You can work them out easily with a calculator.
'77 out of 220 people asked said they liked anchovies on pizza.'
That is $\frac{77}{220}$ as a fraction. To turn it into a percentage key in:

7 7 ÷ 2 2 0 %

You will have the answer 35 which means 35% of the people asked liked anchovies on their pizza!

1

Write these as a percentage.

a) $\frac{62}{100}$

b) 0.32

c) $\frac{7}{10}$

d) 45:100

e) 0.97

Write each percentage as a fraction, ratio and decimal.

	Fraction	Ratio	Decimal			Fraction	Ratio	Decimal
f) 25%				g) 56%				
h) 8%				i) 83%				
j) 12%								

2

What percentage of these patterns has been shaded?

a)

b)

c)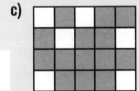

d)

e)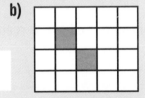

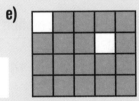

★ *Challenge*

What percentage of this stadium is full of spectators for the Normandy Shields concert?

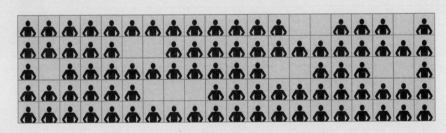

Expressing fractions as percentages

Fractions can be written as percentages. You need to learn these fraction/percentage equivalents.

$\frac{1}{2} = 50\%$ $\frac{1}{4} = 25\%$ $\frac{3}{4} = 75\%$

$\frac{1}{3}$ is nearly 33% ($33\frac{1}{3}\%$) $\frac{2}{3}$ is nearly 66% ($66\frac{2}{3}\%$)

$\frac{1}{10} = 10\%$ $\frac{1}{100} = 1\%$

Write $\frac{7}{10}$ as a percentage.

Have another look. Read the question again.

'$\frac{7}{10}$ as a percentage…'

Ask yourself what they want you to find out.

I need to find the percentage equivalent of $\frac{7}{10}$.

Look at how you can solve it.

Look at the information above…
$\frac{1}{10} = 10\%$
so $\frac{7}{10}$ is 7 x 10% = 70%

Final answer. Is it correct?

Yes, $\frac{7}{10}$ is the same as 70%.
My answer also *looks* correct.

Hints and tips

★ Learn the fraction and percentage equivalents as you would your number bonds and multiplication facts.

★ Other useful fraction/percentage equivalents are:
$\frac{1}{5} = 20\%$ $\frac{2}{5} = 40\%$ $\frac{3}{5} = 60\%$ $\frac{4}{5} = 80\%$
$\frac{1}{8} = 12\frac{1}{2}\%$ $\frac{3}{8} = 37\frac{1}{2}\%$

Write the percentage equivalents of these fractions.
Use the information on the previous page to help you.

a) $\frac{1}{10}$

b) $\frac{2}{8}$

c) $\frac{9}{10}$

d) $\frac{6}{8}$

e) $\frac{5}{10}$

f) $\frac{3}{9}$

g) $\frac{11}{100}$

h) $\frac{6}{9}$

i) $\frac{27}{100}$

j) $\frac{1}{1}$

Reduce these fractions to their lowest form and write their percentage equivalent.

a) $\frac{18}{72}$

b) $\frac{250}{500}$

c) $\frac{48}{64}$

d) $\frac{10}{1000}$

e) $\frac{54}{81}$

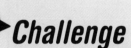

Challenge

a) Ahmed, Joe and Connor were collecting stickers. Out of a total of 1000 stickers, Ahmed had 450, Joe had 225 and Connor had 325. What percentage did each have of the total?

b) Lyn, Sara and Sophie shared their sweets. Out of a total of 200 sweets, Sara had 36, Lyn had 30 and Sophie had 34. What percentage did each have of the total?

Finding simple percentages of whole numbers

Finding a percentage of a quantity is useful when dealing with money.

To find 10% of something you have to divide it by 10.

   10% of 50 = 5

You can then use doubling to find other percentages.

   20% of 50 = 10

   40% of 50 = 20 etc.

What is the price of this car after a 20% discount?

Have another look. Read the question again.

'£500… 20% off…'

Ask yourself what they want you to find out.

I need to find 20% of £500 and then subtract that from £500.

Look at how you can solve it.

10% of 500 is 500 ÷ 10 = 50
So, 20% of 500 = 100 (50 doubled)
£500 − £100 = £400

Final answer. Is it correct?

The price of the car after a 20% discount is £400. I also know that $20\% = \frac{1}{5}$ and a $\frac{1}{5}$ of 500 = 100.

Hints and tips

★ You can use halving to help you find 5%. Find 10% first and then halve the answer. This means you can add the 5%'s and the 10%'s together to find 15%, 25%, 35% etc.

★ To find 1% of a quantity, first find 10% and then find 10% of that answer. You can now find the percentage of any quantity by adding all the 10%'s, 5%'s and 1%'s together!

1

Try these to warm up!

a) Find 10% of £8.

b) Find 10% of 220 kg.

c) Find 10% of £50.

d) Calculate 20% of 400 litres.

e) What is 20% of 200?

f) How much is 40% of 50?

g) What is 40% of 200?

h) Work out 80% of 300 metres.

i) What is 80% of 800?

j) Find 40% of £500.

2

Now try these word problems.

a) There are 25 children in Class 6. If 20% of them are off sick, how many children remain?

b) Frank has £800 to spend on a car. He only spends 80% of his money. How much does Frank spend?

c) Ann-Marie has to travel 800 metres to school. She rides 40% of the distance on her scooter and walks the rest. How far does Ann-Marie walk?

d) Martin wants to give 10% of his savings to his favourite charity. He has saved £190. How much does Martin give to charity?

e) Phoebe ate 80% of a box of chocolates which contained 120 chocolates! How many chocolates did Phoebe eat?

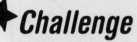

Challenge

The pop star Normandy Shields made £1 000 000 from her first hit – 'Whoops, I've Lost My Bloomers!'

She paid 10% to her agent, 20% to her manager and spent 80% of what was left on clothes.

a) How much did her agent receive?

b) How much did Normandy give her manager?

c) How much did Normandy spend on clothes?

Normandy Shields

Mixed bag – fractions, ratio and proportion

On the right hand page there is a mixture of questions. You will need to use everything you have learnt so far to solve these problems. Look back through the book for help if you need it. Remember to put in the units!

Reduce this fraction to its simplest form. $\frac{16}{96}$

Have another look. Read the question again.

'Reduce... simplest form.'

Ask yourself what they want you to find out.

What is the easiest way of presenting this fraction?

Look at how you can solve it.

What is the highest number that divides into 16 and 96? OK, let's try 8. Two 8s are 16 and twelve 8s are 96. So that gives me $\frac{2}{12}$. I can simplify this further by dividing the top and bottom by 2. My final answer is $\frac{1}{6}$.

Final answer. Is it correct?

$$\frac{1 \ (\times 16)}{6 \ (\times 16)} = \frac{16}{96}$$

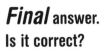

Hints and tips

★ Always approach the problem step-by-step.
★ Draw pictures to help you make sense of the problem.

1

Reduce these fractions to their simplest form.

a) $\frac{4}{12}$

b) $\frac{8}{40}$

c) $\frac{15}{45}$

d) $\frac{20}{120}$

e) $\frac{9}{54}$

Order these fractions on a number line.

f) $\frac{3}{8}$ $\frac{1}{4}$ $\frac{1}{2}$

g) $\frac{2}{7}$ $\frac{2}{3}$ $\frac{3}{7}$

h) $\frac{2}{3}$ $\frac{5}{6}$ $\frac{3}{4}$

i) $\frac{13}{16}$ $\frac{5}{8}$ $\frac{1}{2}$

j) $\frac{1}{5}$ $\frac{3}{10}$ $\frac{7}{20}$

2

Find the fractions of these numbers.

a) $\frac{2}{3}$ of 45

b) $\frac{5}{8}$ of 56

c) $\frac{1}{7}$ of 84

d) $\frac{2}{25}$ of 275

e) $\frac{3}{11}$ of 99

Challenge

a) There are 180 biscuits in my tin. There are 3 custard creams for every 9 bourbons. How many custard creams are there in the tin?

b) What is the ratio of blue squares to white squares in this pattern?

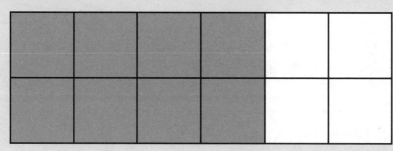

Mixed bag – decimals and percentages

These questions are all about decimals and percentages. You will need to use everything you have learnt so far to solve these problems. Look back through the book for help if you need it. Remember to put in the units!

Put Lloyd's long jumps in order, smallest first.
1.902 m, 1.91 m, 1.891 m, 1.991 m, 1.9 m

Have another look. Read the question again.

'Put... in order...'

Ask yourself what they want to find out.

I need to order these measures by size – longest to shortest.

Look at how you can solve it.

First give all the fractions the same number of decimal places.
I start with the whole numbers. They are all the same. Now I look at the tenths column. Four are 0.9 m, so I look at the hundredths column. 1.991 m is the largest. Keep working methodically.
The order is:
1.891 m, 1.9 m, 1.902 m, 1.91 m, 1.991 m

Final answer. Is it correct?

Check again. Yes, they seem right.

Hints and tips

★ Always approach the problem methodically.
★ When ordering decimals, always give them the same number of decimal places.

Order these decimals largest to smallest.

a) 1.01, 10.1, 11.1, 1.11, 0.1

b) 32.203, 23.032, 33.330, 33.032, 32.223

c) 304.34, 303.033, 304.43, 330.04, 303.303

d) 65.566, 6.065, 6.566, 5.605, 5.656

e) 2.97, 7.209, 7.7, 2.097, 2.779

Convert these fractions to decimals. Try not to use a calculator!

f) $\frac{5}{6}$

g) $\frac{4}{5}$

h) $\frac{3}{8}$

i) $\frac{4}{16}$

j) $\frac{12}{16}$

Write these fractions as percentages.

a) $\frac{46}{100}$

b) $\frac{67}{100}$

c) $\frac{7}{10}$

d) $\frac{2}{5}$

e) $\frac{1}{4}$

 *Challenge*

a) Find 15% of £500.

b) Find 20% of 200.

c) Find 40% of 200.

Answers

Page 9

1
a) $3\frac{3}{4}$ b) $10\frac{1}{3}$ c) $10\frac{1}{3}$ d) $4\frac{4}{13}$
e) $9\frac{1}{5}$ f) $3\frac{1}{11}$ g) $7\frac{7}{8}$ h) $8\frac{5}{9}$
i) $3\frac{2}{13}$ j) $5\frac{5}{9}$

2
a) $\frac{59}{8}$ b) $\frac{945}{13}$ c) $\frac{192}{7}$ d) $\frac{820}{9}$ e) $\frac{323}{6}$

Challenge
a) 87 twelfths of pizza.
b) 86 sixths of cream cake were eaten.
c) $\frac{9}{5}$ of £5 = £9. £9 – £6.50 = £2.50

Page 11

1
a) half as much as b) twice as much as
c) twice as much as d) twice as much as
e) half as much as f) $\frac{1}{4}$
g) $\frac{1}{20}$ h) $\frac{1}{20}$ i) $\frac{1}{9}$ j) $\frac{1}{12}$

2
a) $\frac{1}{5}$ b) $\frac{3}{8}$ c) $\frac{1}{100}$ d) $\frac{1}{50}$ e) $\frac{1}{10}$

Challenge
a) $\frac{1}{3}$ b) $\frac{1}{8}$

Page 13

1
a) $\frac{3}{4}$ b) $\frac{3}{5}$ c) $\frac{1}{2}$ d) $\frac{1}{4}$ e) $\frac{4}{5}$
f) $\frac{7}{10}$ g) $\frac{1}{3}$ h) $\frac{1}{3}$ i) $\frac{1}{3}$ j) $\frac{3}{4}$

2
a) $\frac{5}{6}$ b) $\frac{5}{13}$ c) $\frac{1}{8}$ d) $\frac{2}{7}$ e) $\frac{23}{36}$

Challenge
Answers will vary. Examples: $\frac{1}{3}, \frac{3}{9}, \frac{9}{27}, \frac{10}{30}, \frac{100}{300}, \frac{15}{45},$
$\frac{1}{5}, \frac{3}{15}, \frac{5}{25}, \frac{15}{75}, \frac{100}{500}, \frac{4}{20}, \frac{8}{7}, \frac{24}{21}, \frac{80}{70}, \frac{56}{49}, \frac{32}{28}, \frac{72}{63},$
$\frac{5}{8}, \frac{50}{80}, \frac{15}{24}, \frac{20}{32}, \frac{35}{56}, \frac{45}{72}$

Page 15

1
a) $\frac{3}{4}$ b) $\frac{8}{9}$
c) $\frac{6}{7}$ d) $\frac{3}{7}$
e) $\frac{4}{5}$ f) >
g) < h) < i) < j) <

2
a) $\frac{3}{7}, \frac{2}{5}, \frac{1}{3}$ b) $\frac{5}{7}, \frac{2}{3}, \frac{3}{5}$ c) $\frac{7}{9}, \frac{3}{4}, \frac{5}{8}$ d) $\frac{7}{8}, \frac{4}{5}, \frac{7}{10}$ e) $\frac{7}{10}, \frac{3}{8}, \frac{1}{3}$

Challenge
$1\frac{3}{10}, 1\frac{5}{6}, 2\frac{1}{10}, 2\frac{1}{3}, 2\frac{2}{5}$

Page 17

1
a) 10 b) 35 c) 20 d) 20 e) 49
f) 27 g) 35 h) 55 i) 102 j) 296

2
a) 140 ÷ 7 = 20 20 x 5 = 100 km
b) 54 ÷ 9 = 6 6 x 4 = 24 kg
c) 960 ÷ 8 = 120 120 x 7 = 840 m
d) 1020 ÷ 5 = 205 205 x 3 = 615 cm
e) 1500 ÷ 100 = 15 15 x 7 = 855 l

Challenge
a) 450 m b) 1125 m c) 300 m

Page 19

1

a) 2:1 and $\frac{2}{3}$ b) 3:2 and $\frac{3}{5}$ c) 1:1 and $\frac{1}{2}$

d) 3:3 and $\frac{1}{2}$ e) 1:2 and $\frac{1}{3}$ f) 2:5 and $\frac{2}{7}$

g) 2:2 and $\frac{1}{2}$ h) 3:1 and $\frac{3}{4}$ i) 1:4 and $\frac{1}{5}$

j) 4:1 and $\frac{4}{5}$

2

a) 1:1 and $\frac{1}{2}$ b) 3:2 and $\frac{3}{5}$ c) 1:4 and $\frac{1}{5}$

d) 8:7 and $\frac{8}{15}$ e) 9:7 and $\frac{9}{16}$

Challenge

a) 10 sweets b) 15 boys and 10 girls

c) 30 green balls

Page 21

1

a) 8.6 b) 37.8 c) 16.3 d) 23.48 e) 34.2

g) 74.53 g) 52.9 h) 108.13 i) 71.3 j) 160.22

2

a) 10.966 l b) 59.049 kg c) 11.468 km

d) 72.427 km c) 61.426 kg

Challenge

a) 4.437 km b) 2.26 kg c) 19.782 l

Page 23

1

a) 6 tenths b) 1 hundredth c) 8

d) 5 tenths e) 3 tenths f) 2 hundredths

g) 5 thousandths h) 4 i) 9 tenths

j) 1 thousandth

2

a) 0.428 b) 0.992 c) 18.025

d) 6.006 e) 1.111

Challenge

a) 0.819 + 0.181 = 1 b) 3.18 + 2.3 = 5.48

c) 0.07 + 0.005 + 0.03 + 1 = 1.105

Page 25

1

a) 3.73 b) 11.18 c) 4.27 d) 21.22 e) 10.75

f) 54.44 g) 18.91 h) 29.19 i) 25.56 j) 7.63

2

a) 7.355 b) 673.845 c) 55.555

d) 892.725 e) 11.135

Challenge

a) 8.5: 8.4 and 8.6

   23.35: 23.3 and 23.4

   125.05: 125 and 125.1

b) Possible numbers: 4.677, 4.69, 4.8, 4.95

Page 27

1

a) 44.04, 4.7, 4.44, 4.4

b) 99.9, 98.9, 98.8, 89.9

c) 55.54, 54.5, 45.55, 45.5

d) 42.42, 42.4, 24.42, 24.24

e) 77.22, 72.27, 17.22, 7.27

f) 10.01, 1.01, 0.1, 0.01

g) 61.12, 61.1, 12.66, 12.6

h) 99.09, 9.9, 0.99, 0.09

2

a) 6.667, 6.763, 6.776, 7.675, 7.676, 7.756, 7.765

b) 1.991, 9.119, 9.191, 9.909, 9.919, 9.991, 9.999

c) 5.005, 5.050, 5.055, 5.155, 5.505, 5.550, 5.555

d) 8.448, 48.884, 84.448, 84.484, 84.844, 84.888

Challenge

a) 66.556, 65.465, 64.545, 6.505, 6.445, 6.045.
Difference = 60.511

b) 111.001, 110.101, 101.11, 101.101, 101.011, 11.011.
Difference = 99.99

c) 77.67, 77.55, 76.66, 75.67, 67.57, 55.77.
Difference = 21.9

Page 29

1

a) 3.6 km and 4 km   b) 10.3 km and 10 km

c) 6.9 km and 7 km   d) 52.5 km and 53 km

e) 4.2km and 4 km   f) 24.5 kkm and 25 km

g) 9.8 km and 10 km   h) 89.7 km and 90 km

i) 2.4 km and 2 km   j) 23.4 km and 23 km

2

a) 99.8 and 100   b) 110.7 and 111   c) 899.7 and 900

d) 999.9 and 1000 e) 101 and 101

Challenge

a) No

b) Carol's time of 12.1 seconds was the fastest.

Page 31

1

a) 0.5   b) 0.9   c) 0.3   d) 0.7   e) 0.875

f) 0.375 g) 0.4   h) 0.31   i) 0.8   i) 0.07

2

a) 0.007 b) 0.283 c) 0.027 d) 0.729 e) 0.107

Challenge

a) $\frac{30}{100} = \frac{3}{10} = 0.3$ b) $\frac{35}{100} = \frac{7}{20} = 0.35$

Page 33

a) 0.5   b) 0.75   c) 0.25   d) 0.4   e) 0.2

f) 0.67   g) 0.1   h) 0.3   i) 0.33   j) 0.7

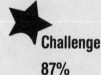

a) 0.25   b) 0.5   c) 0.75   d) 0.1

Challenge

a) 0.25   b) 0.4   c) 0.625

Page 35

1

a) 62%   b) 32%   c) 70%   d) 45%   e) 97%

f) $\frac{1}{4}$ = 1:4 = 0.25   g) $\frac{56}{100}$ = 56:100 = 0.56

h) $\frac{8}{100}$ = 8:100 = 0.08   i) $\frac{83}{100}$ = 83:100 = 0.83

j) $\frac{12}{100}$ = 12:100 = 0.12

2

a) 50%   b) 10%   c) 70%   d) 35%   e) 90%

Challenge

87%

Page 37

1

a) 10%   b) 25%   c) 90%   d) 75%   e) 50%

f) $33\frac{1}{3}$% g) 11%   h) $66\frac{2}{3}$% i) 27%   j) 100%

2

a) $\frac{1}{4}$ and 25%   b) $\frac{1}{2}$ and 50%   c) $\frac{3}{4}$ and 75%

d) $\frac{1}{100}$ and 1%   e) $\frac{2}{3}$ and $66\frac{2}{3}$%

Challenge

a) Ahmed = 45%, Joe = $22\frac{1}{2}$% and Connor $32\frac{1}{2}$%

b) Sara has 18%, Lyn had 15% and Sophie had 17%

Page 39

1

a) 80p b) 22 kg c) 240 m d) £200 e) 40

f) 20 g) 80 h) 240 i) 640 j) 200

2

a) 480 metres b) £640 c) 320 metres

d) £19 e) 96 chocolates

Challenge

a) £100 000 b) £200 000 c) £560 000

Page 41

1

a) $\frac{1}{3}$ b) $\frac{1}{5}$ c) $\frac{1}{3}$ d) $\frac{1}{6}$ e) $\frac{1}{6}$

f) $\frac{1}{4}$, $\frac{3}{8}$, $\frac{1}{2}$ g) $\frac{2}{7}$, $\frac{3}{7}$, $\frac{2}{3}$ h) $\frac{2}{3}$, $\frac{3}{4}$, $\frac{5}{6}$

i) $\frac{1}{2}$, $\frac{5}{8}$, $\frac{13}{16}$ j) $\frac{1}{5}$, $\frac{3}{10}$, $\frac{7}{20}$

2

a) 30 b) 35 c) 12 d) 22 e) 27

Challenge

a) 45 b) 8:4

Page 43

1

a) 11.1, 10.1, 1.11, 1.01, 0.1

b) 33.330, 33.032, 32.223, 32.203, 23.032

c) 330.04, 304.43, 304.34, 303.303, 303.033

d) 65.566, 6.566, 6.065, 5.656, 5.605

e) 7.7, 7.209, 2.97, 2.779, 2.097

f) 0.83

g) 0.8

h) 0.375

i) 0.25

j) 0.75

2

a) 46% b) 67% c) 70% d) 40% e) 25%

Challenge

a) £75 b) 40 c) 80

Your notes